Ye Xi

Ye Xian

The Chinese Cinderella Story,
In Simplified Chinese and Pinyin,
450 Word Vocabulary Level

Written by Jeff Pepper
Chinese Translation by Xiao Hui Wang

Copyright © 2021 – 2022 by Imagin8 Press LLC, all rights reserved.

Published in the United States by Imagin8 Press LLC, Verona, Pennsylvania, US. For information, contact us via email at info@imagin8press.com, or visit www.imagin8press.com.

Our books may be purchased directly in quantity at a reduced price, visit www.imagin8press.com for details.

Imagin8 Press, the Imagin8 logo and the sail image are all trademarks of Imagin8 Press LLC.

Written by Jeff Pepper
Chinese translation by Xiao Hui Wang
Cover and book design by Jeff Pepper
Cover artwork by Paolo Domeniconi, © 2020 Istituto Italiano Edizioni Atlas
Audiobook narration by Junyou Chen

Based on a short story by Duan Chengshi in *Miscellaneous Morsels from Youyang* written around 850 AD

ISBN: 978-1952601187
Version 09.01

Acknowledgements

The tale that we tell in this book is based on a very short story by Duan Chengshi in his book *Miscellaneous Morsels from Youyang* written around 850 AD.

There has been a great deal of scholarly research into the origins, evolution and underlying symbolism of the Cinderella story, and this was incredibly useful to us as we developed this book. Our favorite reference source was Mila Moioli's comprehensive 2018 Ph.D. thesis, *Ye Xian and Her Sisters: The Role of a Tang Story in the Cinderella Cycle*. Her thesis is freely available online, see "Further Reading" at the end of this book.

Thanks also to Choo Suan Hee for proofreading this book, to Junyou Chen for his always-enjoyable audio recording of the book, and Paolo Domeniconi for his beautiful cover artwork.

Audiobook

A complete Chinese language audio version of this book is available free of charge. To access it, go to YouTube.com and search for the Imagin8 Press channel. There you will find free audiobooks for this and all the other books in this series.

You can also visit our website, www.imagin8press.com, to find a direct link to the YouTube audiobook, as well as information about our other books.

Introduction

The story of Cinderella is possibly the most widespread and popular of all folk tales. Over the last two millennia, people from all over the world have told the timeless story of the "cinder maid" in thousands of different ways. But throughout all these versions, the essential elements of the story are unchanged – the highborn but poor and mistreated girl, the wicked stepmother, the magical helpers, the lost shoe, the prince, and the wedding.

It's a powerful and enduring story. But where did it come from, and how did it arrive in China to become the story of Ye Xian that we tell in this book?

Let's start at the beginning. The earliest known version of Cinderella is the Greek story of Rhodopis, which dates from the time of Jesus. Rhodopis (her name means "rosy cheeks") was a beautiful young woman who was bathing one day when an eagle snatched one of her sandals and carried it off to the city of Memphis, dropping it into the lap of the king. The king, amazed by this, sent men across the country to search for the owner of the sandal. When the girl was found, she was brought to the king and made his wife.

Over the next thousand years, this story made its way from Greece to France, where in the 12th century it appears as the story of Le Fresne, the "ash tree girl." A baby girl, one of twins, is abandoned by her mother at a nunnery. She eventually meets and falls in love with a nobleman. Unable to marry him because of her low status, she works for him as a handmaiden. On his wedding night she discovers that he has just married her long-lost twin sister. Her true royal parentage is revealed, she marries the nobleman, and her twin sister marries a different nobleman.

Later, in Italy, a 17th century book of folk tales by Giambattista Basile includes the story of Cenerentola ("cinder girl"), which has all the elements we know from the modern version. She is the daughter of a prince, and is dressed in beautiful clothes by a fairy who lives in a date tree. She meets the king but runs away, leaving her slipper behind. The king tests all the maidens in the land to see whose foot fits the slipper, and when the heroine touches the slipper it jumps from her hand to her foot. The king marries her.

In modern times, everyone knows the story of Cinderella made famous by Walt Disney. Disney's classic is based on two European versions of the story: "Cinderella or the Little Glass Slipper," a French story by Charles Perrault in 1697, and German tale of Aschenputtel by the Brothers Grimm in 1857. Disney reworked the stories to make them more appealing to young American children and their parents. He produced a seven minute animated short film in 1922, followed by the famous full length feature film in 1950 which established the Cinderella images and storyline known throughout the world.

But as the Cinderella story traveled from Greece westward to Europe, it was also carried eastward to Asia along the Silk Road and other ancient trade routes. The story of Ye Xian appeared in *Miscellaneous Morsels from Youyang (Yǒuyáng Zázǔ)*, written by Duan Chengshi in 860 AD, during the Tang Dynasty. This book was an ancient Chinese version of Ripley's Believe It Or Not, a collection of over thirteen hundred assorted legends, stories and tall tales, as well as practical information about herbs and tattoos.

In the book, Duan Chengshi says that the Ye Xian story was told to him by his house servant, a man named Li Shi Yuan from the southern coast of China. The story itself is set a thousand years earlier, around the 3rd century BC, and most of it takes place in what is now China's Guangxi province. However, at the time this area was not actually part of China. It was inhabited by the Zhuang people and was only nominally under Chinese control. Some of the story takes place in a country called Tuohan, which is probably an island off the shores of Malaysia, most likely Java or Sumatra.

Duan Chengshi's original Ye Xian story is very brief, told in just 750 Chinese characters. But the story is quite complex and shows Zhuang, Hindu, Buddhist, and Han Chinese influences.[1]

It's interesting to note that although the Ye Xian story is

---

[1] Beauchamp, Fay. *Asian Origins of Cinderella: The Zhuang Storyteller of Guangxi.* 2010. Retrieved from https://web.archive.org/web/20171215135835/http://journal.or altradition.org/files/articles/25ii/10_25.2.pdf

1200 years old and comes from southern China, it has all the main elements of the modern Cinderella story, and matches it more closely than later European versions. The heroine, Ye Xian, is the daughter of the village chief, not quite a princess but close. Her mother and father both die, leaving her in the hands of her cruel stepmother. She has magical helpers: a fish who is really her mother returned to earth to help her, and a mysterious flying man whose identity is never really explained. She goes to the Cave Festival, equivalent to Cinderella's ball. There is the famous lost slipper, made of gold thread and silk instead of glass. There is a king who obtains the slipper and attempts to find its owner. There is the magic of the slipper itself, preventing anyone but its owner from wearing it. And of course, there is the eventual marriage of the heroine and the punishment of the evildoers.

But unlike Disney's Cinderella, the Ye Xian story does not simply end with the heroine marrying and living happily ever after. This is similar to other versions, especially Grimm's, but we won't give away the ending here!

If this quick historical overview piques your interest, you'll be happy to learn that there's much more to read on the subject. Many scholars have written extensively about the origins and symbolism of the Ye Xian story. Please see the "Further Reading" section at the back of this book to learn more.

One final note. In telling this story we've used just 450

Chinese words, most of which are in the standard 1200-word HSK4 vocabulary. This has cramped our storytelling style a bit, but we hope it makes it easier for beginning and intermediate students of Chinese to read and enjoy the book. Whenever we use a word that's not in HSK4, that word is defined where it first occurs. All words used in the book are included in the glossary at the end, along with an English translation of the story.

A free audiobook version of this book is available on YouTube, on the Imagin8 Press channel. Visit our website, www.imagin8press.com, to find a direct link to the audiobook.

We hope you enjoy this story!

Jeff Pepper and Xiao Hui Wang
Pittsburgh, Pennsylvania

Ye Xian

叶限

Yè Xiàn

Wǒ qīn'ài de háizimen, ràng wǒ gàosù nǐmen yígè cóng wǒ mǔqīn nàlǐ tīng dào de gùshì. Tā cóng tā de mǔqīn nàlǐ tīngdào le zhège gùshì, tā de mǔqīn cóng yígè míngjiào Lǐ de nánrén nàlǐ tīngdào le zhège gùshì. Hěnjiǔ yǐqián, Lǐ shì zài wǒ yéye nǎinai jiā gōngzuò. Tā shì cóng Zhōngguó de nánfāng lái de. Tā zhīdào xǔduō zhù zài nà'er de Zhuàng rén liú xiàlái de shén guài gùshì. Zhè shì tā gàosù wǒ nǎinai de gùshì. Wǒ juédé nǐmen huì xǐhuān tā de!

叶限

我亲爱[2]的孩子们，让我告诉你们一个
从我母亲那里听到的故事。她从她的
母亲那里听到了这个故事，她的母亲
从一个名叫李的男人那里听到了这个
故事。很久以前，李是在我爷爷奶奶
家工作。他是从中国的南方来的。他
知道许多住在那儿的壮人留下来的
神[3]怪故事。这是他告诉我奶奶的故
事。我觉得你们会喜欢它的！

---

[2] 亲爱　　qīn'ài – dear

[3] 神　　' shén – god, spirit

Zhè shì yígè hěnjiǔ yǐqián de gùshì, zài Qín hé Hàn zhīqián. Dāngshí yǒurén zhù zài wǒmen xiànzài jiào Guǎngxī de dìfāng. Zhèxiē rén jiào tāmen zìjǐ wéi Zhuàng. Zài zhège dìfāng yǒu yígè cūnzhuāng jiào Wú cūn. Wú cūn de rénmen dàbùfèn shēnghuó zài jìn hǎiyáng de shān dòng lǐ. Tāmen zài shānlǐ chī yú hé zhòng dàmǐ. Cūnzhǎng shì yígè jiào Wú Dōng de rén.

Wú Dōng yǒu liǎng gè qīzi. Zhè zài dāngshí de Zhuàng zhǎnglǎo lǐ hěn pǔbiàn. Wǒmen bù zhīdào tā de dìyīgè qīzi de míngzì, dànshì wǒmen zhīdào tā yǒu yígè nǚ'ér, yí gè míngjiào Yè Xiàn de nǚhái. Yè Xiàn hěn měilì, hěn cōngming. Tā hái yǒu hěnduō jìnéng. Tā néng

这是一个很久以前的故事，在秦和汉之前[4]。当时有人住在我们现在叫广西的地方。这些人叫他们自己为壮。在这个地方有一个村庄[5]叫吴村。吴村的人们大部分生活在近海洋的山洞[6]里。他们在山里吃鱼和种[7]大米。村长是一个叫吴东的人。

吴东有两个妻子。这在当时的壮长老里很普遍。我们不知道他的第一个妻子的名字，但是我们知道她有一个女儿，一个名叫叶限的女孩。叶限很美丽，很聪明。她还有很多技能。她能

---

[4] The Qin (221-206 BC) and Han (202 BC-220 AD) Dynasties
[5] 村庄　　cūnzhuāng – village
[6] 洞　　　dòng – cave
[7] 种　　　zhòng – to grow

zuò nǚrén de gōngzuò, lìrú zuò yīfu, zuò fàn hé dǎsǎo. Tā hái zhīdào zěnme bǎ jīnzi biàn chéng měilì de jīn xiàn.

Wú Dōng de dì èr gè qīzi jiào Jīn. Jīn yǒu zìjǐ de nǚ'ér jiào Jùnlì, bǐ Yè Xiàn niánqīng. Jùnlì bù xǐhuān gōngzuò, duì jiějie Yè Xiàn yě bù zūnzhòng.

Wú Dōng shì yígè hǎo de cūnzhǎng, yěshì yígè hǎorén. Tā ài tā de liǎng gè qīzi hé liǎng gè nǚ'ér. Dànshì tā de dì yī gè qīzi sǐ le, jǐ nián yǐhòu, Wú Dōng yě shēngbìng le, sǐ le.

做女人的工作，例如做衣服，做饭和打扫。她还知道怎么把金[8]子变成美丽的金线[9]。

吴东的第二个妻子叫金。金有自己的女儿叫俊丽，比叶限年轻。俊丽不喜欢工作，对姐姐叶限也不尊重。

吴东是一个好的村长，也是一个好人。他爱他的两个妻子和两个女儿。但是他的第一个妻子死了，几年以后，吴东也生病了，死了。

---

[8] 金   jīn – gold, golden
[9] 线   xiàn – thread

Zài Zhuàng rén nàlǐ, cūnzhǎng sǐ le yǐhòu, tā de dà érzi jiù chéngwéi xīn de cūnzhǎng. Dànshì Wú Dōng méiyǒu érzi. Yīncǐ, Wú rén zhǐ néng ràng lìng yìjiā de rén chūlái dāng xīn cūnzhǎng.

Yè Xiàn, Jīn hé Jùnlì yǐqián dōu shì cūnzhǎng jiālǐ de rén. Dànshì dāng Wú Dōng sǐ le, xīn cūnzhǎng shàngwèi yǐhòu, tāmen búshì tā jiā de rén. Tāmen shénme dōu méiyǒu le. Tāmen zhǐ nénglíkāi cūnzhǎng zhù de dà fángzi. Tāmen xiàng cūn lǐ de qítā rén yíyàng, zhù zài shān lǐ de yígè xiǎo shāndòng lǐ. Tāmen bìxū zìjǐ qù zhuā yú, zìjǐ zhòng dàmǐ.

Jīn ài zìjǐ de nǚ'ér, dàn tā bú ài Yè Xiàn. Tā ràng Yè Xiàn chéngwéi tā jiā de púrén. Tā ràng Yè Xiàn zuò

在壮人那里，村长死了以后，他的大儿子就成为新的村长。但是吴东没有儿子。因此，吴人只能让另一家的人出来当新村长。

叶限，金和俊丽以前都是村长家里的人。但是当吴东死了，新村长上位以后，他们不是他家的人。他们什么都没有了。他们只能离开村长住的大房子。他们像村里的其他人一样，住在山里的一个小山洞里。他们必须自己去抓[10]鱼，自己种大米。

金爱自己的女儿，但她不爱叶限。她让叶限成为她家的仆人[11]。她让叶限做

---

[10] 抓   zhuā – to grab
[11] 仆人   púrén – servant

suǒyǒu de zuò fàn hé dǎsǎo gōngzuò, dàn tā hái gěi Yè Xiàn zuò qítā gèng wēixiǎn de gōngzuò. Yǒu de shíhòu, Yè Xiàn bìxū cóng shān lǐ wēixiǎn de dìfāng ná mùchái. Yǒu de shíhòu, tā bìxū cóng shēn jǐng lǐ qǔ shuǐ. Dànshì Yè Xiàn méiyǒu shuō shénme. Tā měitiān nǔlì gōngzuò. Tā méiyǒu péngyǒu, méiyǒu shíjiān wán huòzhě xuéxí.

Yǒu yìtiān, Jīn ràng Yè Xiàn qù shēn jǐng lǐ qǔ shuǐ. Yè Xiàn zǒu dào jǐng nà'er, qǔ le yì tǒng shuǐ. Tā kàndào shuǐtǒng lǐ yǒu dōngxi. Tā gèng zǐxì de kàn, fāxiàn nà shì yìtiáo xiǎo yú. Nà tiáo yú cháng liǎng cùn, yǒu hóngsè de qí hé jīnsè de yǎnjīng. Tā juédé nà tiáo yú

所有的做饭和打扫工作，但她还给叶限做其他更危险的工作。有的时候，叶限必须从山里危险的地方拿木柴[12]。有的时候，她必须从深井[13]里取水。但是叶限没有说什么。她每天努力工作。她没有朋友，没有时间玩或者学习。

有一天，金让叶限去深井里取水。叶限走到井那儿，取了一桶[14]水。她看到水桶里有东西。她更仔细地看，发现那是一条小鱼。那条鱼长两寸[15]，有红色的鳍[16]和金色的眼睛。她觉得那条鱼

---

[12] 木柴　　mùchái – firewood
[13] 井　　　jǐng – well
[14] 桶　　　tǒng – bucket
[15] 寸　　　cùn – a Chinese inch, about 1.5"
[16] 鳍　　　qí – fin

hěn měilì. Tā bù zhīdào nà tiáo yú qíshí shì tā sǐqù de mǔqīn, tā de mǔqīn huí dào rénshì lái bāngzhù tā de nǚ'ér.

Yè Xiàn méiyǒu rènhé péngyǒu, suǒyǐ tā juédìng nà tiáo xiǎo yú kěyǐ chéngwéi tā de péngyǒu. Yúshì tā bǎ yú fàng zài wǎn lǐ. Tā méiyǒu gàosù tā de jìmǔ hé tā de jìmèi guānyú yú de shì.

Měitiān tā dōuhuì bǎ tā zìjǐ chī de dōngxi fēn yìdiǎn gěi nà tiáo yú, měitiān yú dōu huì chī wán tā gěi de dōngxi, huì zhǎng dà yìxiē. Guò le bùjiǔ, nà tiáo yú tài dà le, nà zhǐ wǎn fàng búxià tā le, suǒyǐ Yè Xiàn bǎ yú fàng dào le yígè gèng dà de wǎn lǐ, ránhòu yòu shì yígè gèng dà de wǎn, ránhòu shì yígè dà tǒng. Yú réngrán zài zhǎng dà. Hěn kuài, méiyǒu gèng dà

很美丽。她不知道那条鱼其实是她死
去的母亲，她的母亲回到人世来帮助
她的女儿。

叶限没有任何朋友，所以她决定那条
小鱼可以成为她的朋友。于是她把鱼
放在碗里。她没有告诉她的继母和她
的继妹关于鱼的事。

每天她都会把她自己吃的东西分一点
给那条鱼，每天鱼都会吃完她给的东
西，会长大一些。过了不久，那条鱼
太大了，那只碗放不下它了，所以叶
限把鱼放到了一个更大的碗里，然后
又是一个更大的碗，然后是一个大桶
。鱼仍然在长大。很快，没有更大

de dōngxi kěyǐ fàng xià yú le. Yúshì Yè Xin bǎ yú fàng zài shuǐ táng lǐ. Yú zhǎng a zhǎng a, yìzhí zhǎng dào chàbùduō shí chǐ cháng.

Měitiān, Yè Xiàn dōu gěi yú chī de dōngxi. Tā bǎ chī de dōngxi tuī dào shuǐ lǐ, zhèyàng yú jiù kěyǐ chī le. Měi dāng Yè Xiàn lái dào shuǐ táng de shíhòu, yú de tóu jiù shēn chū shuǐ miàn, bǎ tóu fàng zài shuǐ táng biān. Yè Xiàn jiù bǎ tā de tóu fàng zài yú de tóu shàng, táitóu kànzhe tiān, bìngqiě hé yú shuōhuà. Nǚhái gàosù yú tā de wèntí hé tā de mèngxiǎng. Yú tīngzhe, dànshì cóng bù shuōhuà.

的东西可以放下鱼了。于是叶限把鱼放在水塘[17]里。鱼长啊长啊，一直长到差不多十尺长。

每天，叶限都给鱼吃的东西。她把吃的东西推到水里，这样鱼就可以吃了。每当叶限来到水塘的时候，鱼的头就伸[18]出水面，把头放在水塘边。叶限就把她的头放在鱼的头上，抬头看着天，并且和鱼说话。女孩告诉鱼她的问题和她的梦想。鱼听着，但是从不说话。

---

[17] 塘　　　táng – pond
[18] 伸　　　shēn – to stretch out

Yè Xiàn ài nà tiáo yú, ér nà tiáo yú yě ài Yè Xiàn. Dànshì yú hěn xiǎoxīn. Rúguǒ yǒu qítā rén zǒu jìn shuǐ táng, yú huì yóu xiàqù, cáng zài shuǐ táng dǐ.

Yǒu yìtiān, jìmǔ zài fángzi lǐ wǎng wài kàn, kàndào Yè Xiàn hé nà tiáo yú zài yìqǐ. Tā bù míngbai nǚhái hé yú zài zuò shénme, dànshì tā xǐhuān chī yú. Suǒyǐ, jìmǔ děng Yè Xiàn huí dào fángzi lǐ yǐhòu, jiù qù le shuǐ táng biān kàn yú. Dànshì yú cáng zài shuǐ táng dǐ, jíshǐ Jīn zǒu jìn le kàn, tā yě kàn bú dào yú.

Jìmǔ zhēn de hěn xiǎng bǎ yú zhuā le chī. Yúshì tā duì Yè Xiàn shuō, "Wǒ qīn'ài de nǚ'ér, nǐ gōngzuò tài xīnkǔ le. Wǒ xiǎng gěi nǐ yí jiàn xīn wàiyī. Tuō xià

叶限爱那条鱼，而那条鱼也爱叶限。但是鱼很小心。如果有其他人走近水塘，鱼会游下去，藏[19]在水塘底。

有一天，继母在房子[20]里往外看，看到叶限和那条鱼在一起。她不明白女孩和鱼在做什么，但是她喜欢吃鱼。所以，继母等叶限回到房子里以后，就去了水塘边看鱼。但是鱼藏在水塘底，即使金走近了看，她也看不到鱼。

继母真的很想把鱼抓了吃。于是她对叶限说，"我亲爱的女儿，你工作太辛苦了。我想给你一件新外衣。脱下

---

19 藏　　　cáng – to hide
20 房子　　fángzi – house

nǐ de jiù yīfu, chuān shàng zhè jiàn piàoliang de xīn wàiyī." Yè Xiàn hěn gāoxìng yǒu xīn yīfu, suǒyǐ tuō xià le tā de jiù yīfu, chuān shàng le wàiyī. "Nǐ kànqǐlái hěn měi," jìmǔ yòng tiántián de shēngyīn shuō, "xiànzài qù shān jiǎo xià de jǐng lǐ qǔ shuǐ." Zhè kǒu jǐng yǒu jǐ lǐ yuǎn, dànshì Yè Xiàn ànzhào tā shuō de qù zuò.

Děng nǚhái zǒu dé kànbùjiàn le, jìmǔ mǎshàng tuō xià zìjǐ de yīfu, chuān shàng nǚhái de yīfu. Ránhòu tā ná qǐ yì bǎ dāo, bǎ tā cáng zài xiùzi lǐ. Tā qù le shuǐ táng, jiàozhe yú. Yú kànjiàn le jìmǔ, dàn yǐwéi shì Yè Xiàn, suǒyǐ bǎ tóu shēn chū shuǐmiàn. Jìmǔ hěn kuài yòng dāo shā sǐ le yú. Ránhòu, tā bǎ yú ná jìn wūzi, yòng yú zuò le wǎnfàn, ránhòu chī

你的旧衣服，穿上这件漂亮的新外衣。"叶限很高兴有新衣服，所以脱下了她的旧衣服，穿上了外衣。"你看起来很美，"继母用甜甜的声音说，"现在去山脚下的井里取水。"这口井有几里远，但是叶限按照她说的去做。

等女孩走得看不见了，继母马上脱下自己的衣服，穿上女孩的衣服。然后她拿起一把刀，把它藏在袖²¹子里。她去了水塘，叫着鱼。鱼看见了继母，但以为是叶限，所以把头伸出水面。继母很快用刀杀死了鱼。然后，她把鱼拿进屋子，用鱼做了晚饭，然后吃

---

²¹ 袖　　　xiù – sleeve

le tā. Zhè shì yí dùn fēicháng hǎochī de fàn, tā bǐ qítā de yú yào hǎochī liǎng bèi.

Jìmǔ bùxiǎng ràng Yè Xiàn zhīdào tā zuò de shìqíng. Yúshì tā bǎ yú gǔ rēng jìn le fángzi hòumiàn de fèn duī lǐ. Érqiě tā méiyǒu gěi Yè Xiàn liú rènhé chī de dōngxi. Ér zhǐshì gěi le Yè Xiàn yìxiē mǐfàn.

Dì èr tiān, Yè Xiàn huídào shuǐ táng qù kàn tā de péngyǒu, nà tiáo yú. Tā yícì yòu yícì de jiàozhe nà tiáo yú, dànshì nà tiáo yú méiyǒu chūxiàn. Guò le hěn cháng shíjiān, tā zhīdào nà tiáo yú bùjiàn le. Tā zuò zài shuǐ táng biān, kū le.

了它。这是一顿非常好吃的饭，它比其他的鱼要好吃两倍。

继母不想让叶限知道她做的事情。于是她把鱼骨[22]扔进了房子后面的粪[23]堆[24]里。而且她没有给叶限留任何吃的东西。而只是给了叶限一些米饭。

第二天，叶限回到水塘去看她的朋友，那条鱼。她一次又一次地叫着那条鱼，但是那条鱼没有出现。过了很长时间，她知道那条鱼不见了。她坐在水塘边，哭了。

---

[22] 骨　　gǔ – bone
[23] 粪　　fèn – manure
[24] 堆　　duī – a heap or pile

Túrán, tā tīngdào le yígè shēngyīn. Tā táitóu kàn, kàndào yígè rén zài tiānshàng fēi. Nà rén fēi xiàlái, zhàn zài tā qiánmiàn. Tā hěn gāo, chuānzhe báisè cháng yī, tā yǒu cháng cháng de bái fà, báifà fēi xiàng gège fāngxiàng.

Nàge rén duì Yè Xiàn shuō, "Bié kū. Nǐ de jìmǔ shā le nà tiáo yú, zài zuó wǎn de wǎnfàn shàng chī le tā. Tā bǎ gǔtou rēng jìn fèn duī lǐ. Qù nàlǐ zhǎo yú de gǔtou. Bǎ tāmen cáng zài nǐ de fángjiān lǐ. Bǎ gǔtou fàng zài sì gè guànzi lǐ, bǎ nàxiē guànzi fàng zài chuáng de sì gè jiǎo xiàmiàn. Wǒ bìxū gàosù nǐ, nà shì yìtiáo yǒu mófǎ de yú, tā de gǔtou shì yǒu mófǎ de. Rúguǒ nǐ xūyào rènhé dōngxi,

突然，她听到了一个声音。她抬头
看，看到一个人在天上飞。那人飞下
来，站在她前面。他很高，穿着白色
长衣，他有长长的白发，白发飞向各
个方向。

那个人对<u>叶限</u>说，"别哭。你的继母
杀了那条鱼，在昨晚的晚饭上吃了
它。她把骨头扔进粪堆里。去那里找
鱼的骨头。把它们藏在你的房间里。
把骨头放在四个罐[25]子里，把那些罐子
放在床的四个角下面。我必须告诉
你，那是一条有魔法[26]的鱼，它的骨头
是有魔法的。如果你需要任何东西，

---

25 罐　　　guàn – pot
26 魔法　　mófǎ – magic

zhǐ xū xiàng shàngtiān qídǎo, gǔtou huì bāngzhù nǐ dédào nǐ xiǎng yào de dōngxi."

Nǚhái ànzhào nà rén shuō de qù zuò. Tā qù le fèn duī, zhǎodào le yú de gǔtou. Tā shōushí qǐ suǒyǒu de gǔtou, bǎ tāmen bān jìn tā de fángjiān, cáng zài chuángxià de sì gè guànzi lǐ.

Tā fēicháng è, dànshì tā dāngrán bùxiǎng chī jìmǔ zhǔnbèi de yú. Yúshì tā xiàng shàngtiān qídǎo gěi tā chī de dōngxi. Zài tā de qiánmiàn mǎshàng chūxiàn le yì guō hǎo chī de cài jiǎozi. Tā chī le suǒyǒu de jiǎozi. Ránhòu tā xiàng shàngtiān qídǎo, gěi tā yìxiē piàoliang de xīn yīfu, yīfu yě chūxiàn le. Tā chuān shàng yīfu. Ránhòu tā shǒu lǐ názhe yímiàn xiǎo jìngzi, kànzhe tā

只需向上天祈祷[27]，骨头会帮助你得到你想要的东西。"

女孩按照那人说的去做。她去了粪堆，找到了鱼的骨头。她收拾起所有的骨头，把它们搬进她的房间，藏在床下的四个罐子里。

她非常饿，但是她当然不想吃继母准备的鱼。于是她向上天祈祷给她吃的东西。在她的前面马上出现了一锅好吃的菜饺子。她吃了所有的饺子。然后她向上天祈祷，给她一些漂亮的新衣服，衣服也出现了。她穿上衣服。然后她手里拿着一面小镜子，看着她

---

[27] 祈祷　　　qídǎo – prayer

zì jǐ. Tā duì zìjǐ shuō, "Wǒ xiǎng yǒu le zhèxiē piàoliang de yīfu, wǒ kěyǐ qù cānjiā Dòng Jié le!"

Yì nián yícì de Dòng Jié shì zài xià gè xīngqī. Fùjìn suǒyǒu cūnzhuāng de niánqīng rén dōu lái cānjiā zhège jiérì, chànggē tiàowǔ, yǔ qítā niánqīng rén jiànmiàn, bìngqiě zhǎo yígè kěyǐ jiéhūn de rén. Yè Xiàn zhēn de hěn xiǎng qù cānjiā Dòng Jié, dànshì tā de jìmǔ jiào tā liú zài jiālǐ. Zhè shì yīnwèi Jīn xīwàng tā zìjǐ de nǚ'ér zhǎodào hǎo zhàngfu, tā bù xīwàng cōngming měilì de Yè Xiàn zài tāmen de fùjìn. "Nǐ liú zài zhèlǐ," Jīn duì Yè Xiàn shuō. "Kànzhe yuànzi lǐ de guǒshù, yào bǎozhèng méi rén ná zǒu wǒmen de shuǐguǒ."

自己。她对自己说，"我想有了这些漂亮的衣服，我可以去参加洞节了！"

一年一次的洞节是在下个星期。附近所有村庄的年轻人都来参加这个节日，唱歌跳舞，与其他年轻人见面，并且找一个可以结婚的人。叶限真的很想去参加洞节，但是她的继母叫她留在家里。这是因为金希望她自己的女儿找到好丈夫，她不希望聪明美丽的叶限在她们的附近。"你留在这里，"金对叶限说。"看着院子[28]里的果树，要保证没人拿走我们的水果。"

---

[28] 院子　　yuànzi – courtyard

Yè Xiàn shì gè hǎo nǚ'ér. Tā zǒngshì xiǎng yào duì jìmǔ biǎoshì shífēn zūnzhòng, zuò jìmǔ ràng tā zuò de yíqiè shìqíng. Dànshì tā zhēn de hěn xiǎng qù cānjiā Dòng Jié. "Wǒ yīnggāi zěnme bàn?" Tā wèn tā zìjǐ. Tā juédìng xiàng shàngtiān qídǎo, gěi tā yí jiàn piàoliang yīfu chuān qù cānjiā Dòng Jié. Rúguǒ shàngtiān bǎ yīfu gěi tā, nà tā jiù huì qù. Rúguǒ méiyǒu, nà tā huì liú zài jiālǐ, kànzhe yuànzi lǐ de guǒshù.

Yè Xiàn děngdào tā de jìmǔ hé jìmèi dōu zǒu dé kànbùjiàn le. Ránhòu, tā zuò zài yú gǔtou qiánmiàn, xiàng shàngtiān qídǎo gěi tā yí jiàn piàoliang yīfu chuān qù cānjiā Dòng Jié. Tā mǎshàng jiù shōudào le yí jiàn piàoliang de lánlǜsè sīchóu cháng yī, yìtiáo yòng cuì niǎo yǔmáo

叶限是个好女儿。她总是想要对继母表示十分尊重，做继母让她做的一切事情。但是她真的很想去参加洞节。

"我应该怎么办？"她问她自己。她决定向上天祈祷，给她一件漂亮衣服穿去参加洞节。如果上天把衣服给她，那她就会去。如果没有，那她会留在家里，看着院子里的果树。

叶限等到她的继母和继妹都走得看不见了。然后，她坐在鱼骨头前面，向上天祈祷给她一件漂亮衣服穿去参加洞节。她马上就收到了一件漂亮的蓝绿色丝绸[29]长衣，一条用翠鸟[30]羽毛[31]

---

[29] 丝绸　　sīchóu – silk
[30] 翠鸟　　cuì niǎo – kingfisher
[31] 羽毛　　yǔmáo – feather

zuò de dǒupéng, hé yìshuāng yòng jīn sīxiàn zuò de tuōxié. Tā gāoxìng de kū le. Tā chuān shàng xīn yīfu, qù le Dòng Jié. Cānjiā Dòng Jié de rénmen kànjiàn le tā, yǐwéi tā shì yí wèi měilì de gōngzhǔ, xǔduō nánrén dōu xiǎng hé tā jiéhūn.

Dāngrán, Jīn hé tā de nǚ'ér Jùnlì yě zài Dòng Jié, Jīn xiǎng wèi Jùnlì zhǎodào yígè hǎo zhàngfu. Jīn hé yìxiē niánqīngrén shuōzhe tā de nǚ'ér. Jùnlì túrán tái qǐ tóu, kànjiàn le Yè Xiàn. Tā duì tā de mǔqīn shuō, "Kànjiàn nà biān chuānzhe cuì niǎo yǔmáo zuò de dǒupéng de nǚhái le ma? Tā shìbúshì zhǎng dé hěn xiàng wǒ de jiějiě?" Jìmǔ kàn le kàn, yě kànjiàn le

做的斗篷[32]，和一双用金丝线做的
拖鞋[33]。她高兴地哭了。她穿上新衣
服，去了洞节。参加洞节的人们看见
了她，以为她是一位美丽的公主[34]，许
多男人都想和她结婚。

当然，金和她的女儿俊丽也在洞节，
金想为俊丽找到一个好丈夫。金和一
些年轻人说着她的女儿。俊丽突然抬
起头，看见了叶限。她对她的母亲
说，"看见那边穿着翠鸟羽毛做的斗
篷的女孩了吗？她是不是长得很像我
的姐姐？"继母看了看，也看见了

---

[32] 斗篷 dǒupéng – cloak
[33] 拖鞋 tuōxié – slipper
[34] 公主 gōngzhǔ – princess

tā.

Yè Xiàn zhīdào tāmen zài kàn tā. Yúshì tā zhuǎnshēn fēikuài de pǎo zǒu le. Tā pǎo dé tài kuài, yì zhǐ jīn tuōxié cóng tā de jiǎo shàng diào le xiàlái. Tā zhǐ chuān le yì zhǐ tuōxié pǎo huí le jiā. Dāng tā pǎo dào jiā shí, tā fēicháng lèi ér méiyǒu jìn dòng lǐ. Tā zhǐshì bǎ yìtiáo jiù dǒupéng bāo zài shēnshàng, zǒu dào yuànzi lǐ tā mǔqīn de fénmù qián. Ránhòu, tā tǎng zài dìshàng, shuāng bì bàozhe tā mǔqīn fénmù shàng de guǒshù, shuìzháo le.

Nàtiān wǎnshàng, jìmǔ hé jìnǚ huí dào le jiā. Tāmen liǎ dōu kàn dào Yè Xiàn zài yuànzi lǐ bàozhe guǒshù shuì

她。

叶限知道他们在看她。于是她转身[35]飞快地跑走了。她跑得太快，一只金拖鞋从她的脚上掉了下来。她只穿了一只拖鞋跑回了家。当她跑到家时，她非常累而没有进洞里。她只是把一条旧斗篷包在身上，走到院子里她母亲的坟墓[36]前。然后，她躺在地上，双臂[37]抱着她母亲坟墓上的果树，睡着[38]了。

那天晚上，继母和继女回到了家。他们俩都看到叶限在院子里抱着果树睡

---

[35] 转身　zhuǎnshēn – to turn around
[36] 坟墓　fénmù – grave
[37] 臂　bì – arm
[38] 睡着　shuìzhào – asleep

jiào. Tāmen rènwéi tā bù kěnéng qùguò Dòng Jié, suǒyǐ tāmen bú zài xiǎng zhè jiàn shì le.

Yè Xiàn zài Dòng Jié de shíhòu, cūnlǐ de yí wèi nóngfū yě zài nàlǐ, zài hé yìxiē péngyǒu liáotiān, lí Yè Xiàn zhàn de dìfāng bù yuǎn. Nóngfū kànjiàn Yè Xiàn pǎo zǒu, tā yě kànjiàn jīn tuōxié cóng tā de jiǎo shàng diào xiàlái. Yúshì tā zǒu guòqù ná qǐ tuōxié. Tā kànzhe tuōxié, fāxiàn tā shì yòng jīn sīxiàn zuò de, suǒyǐ tā zhīdào tā hěn guìzhòng. Tā juédìng shìzhe bǎ tuōxié mài le.

Dànshì tā yīnggāi zài nǎlǐ mài, yòu yīnggāi mài gěi shuí ne? Tā duì zhège wèntí xiǎng le hěnjiǔ. Tā xūyào zhǎodào yígè bú huì wèn tuōxié shì cóng nǎlǐ lái de

觉。他们认为她不可能去过洞节，所以他们不再想这件事了。

叶限在洞节的时候，村里的一位农夫[39]也在那里，在和一些朋友聊天，离叶限站的地方不远。农夫看见叶限跑走，他也看见金拖鞋从她的脚上掉下来。于是他走过去拿起拖鞋。他看着拖鞋，发现它是用金丝线做的，所以他知道它很贵重。他决定试着把拖鞋卖了。

但是他应该在哪里卖，又应该卖给谁呢？他对这个问题想了很久。他需要找到一个不会问拖鞋是从哪里来的

---

[39] 农夫　　　nóngfū – farmer

fù rén. Ránhòu tā túrán zhīdào tā yīnggāi zěnme zuò. Tā kěyǐ qù Tuóhàn, nà shì zài hǎiyáng lìng yìbiān de yígè dàguó. Tā tīng biérén shuō Tuóhàn guówáng shì yígè niánqīngrén, fēicháng qiángdà, fēicháng yǒu qián, tā yǒu hěnduō bīng. Nóngfū hái tīng biérén shuō, Tuóhàn guówáng ài měilì de dōngxi duōguò ài rénmen.

Yúshì, nóngfū gěi le chuánfū yìxiē qián, dài tā guò hǎi qù Tuóhàn. Lùshàng zǒu le sān tiān. Dāng tā lái dào Tuóhàn shí, tā ná qián gěi le yìxiē rén, ràng tāmen bǎ tā jièshào gěi guówáng.

"Nǐ shì shuí, nǐ wèishénme zài zhèlǐ?" guówáng wèn.

富人。然后他突然知道他应该怎么做。他可以去陀汗，那是在海洋另一边的一个大国。他听别人说陀汗国王是一个年轻人，非常强大，非常有钱，他有很多兵[40]。农夫还听别人说，陀汗国王爱美丽的东西多过爱人们。

于是，农夫给了船夫一些钱，带他过海去陀汗。路上走了三天。当他来到陀汗时，他拿钱给了一些人，让他们把他介绍给国王。

"你是谁，你为什么在这里？"国王问。

---

[40] 兵　　　bīng – soldier

"Wěidà de guówáng, wǒ yǒuxiē dōngxi wǒ xiǎng nǐ huì yǒu xìngqù de." Nóngfū huídá. Ránhòu tā bǎ tuōxié gěi guówáng kàn.

Guówáng kàn dào le tuōxié, mǎshàng jiù ài shàng le tā. Tuōxié xiàng tàiyáng yíyàng liàng, yòu xiàng yǔmáo yíyàng qīng, tā bù fāchū rènhé shēngyīn, shènzhì zài shítou shàng yě bú huì yǒu shēngyīn. Guówáng cóng nóngfū nàlǐ mǎi le tuōxié. Ránhòu guówáng xiǎng, "Zhè zhī tuōxié zhēn piàoliang, bù zhīdào zuò tuōxié hé chuānzhe tuōxié de nàgè nǚrén yǒu duō měilì!" Yīncǐ, tā juédìng zhǎodào zuò tuōxié de nǚrén.

Tā jiào gōng lǐ de měi gè nǚrén dōu shì chuān nà zhǐ tuōxié. Dànshì tuōxié yǒu mólì. Tā huì gǎibiàn tā de dà

"伟大[41]的国王，我有些东西我想你会有兴趣的。"农夫回答。然后他把拖鞋给国王看。

国王看到了拖鞋，马上就爱上了它。拖鞋像太阳一样亮，又像羽毛一样轻，它不发出任何声音，甚至在石头上也不会有声音。国王从农夫那里买了拖鞋。然后国王想，"这只拖鞋真漂亮，不知道做拖鞋和穿着拖鞋的那个女人有多美丽！"因此，他决定找到做拖鞋的女人。

他叫宫[42]里的每个女人都试穿那只拖鞋。但是拖鞋有魔力。它会改变它的大

---

[41] 伟大　　wěidà – great
[42] 宫　　　gōng – palace

xiǎo, suǒyǐ, měi dāng yǒu nǚrén shìzhe chuān shàng tuōxié, tuōxié jiù huì biàn dé bǐ nǚrén de jiǎo xiǎo yícùn! Yīncǐ, méiyǒu yígè rén néng chuān shàng tā.

Guówáng méiyǒu fàngqì. Tā jiào Tuóhàn de měi gè nǚrén dōu shì chuān tuōxié. Wángguó zhōng de měi gè nǚrén dōu yígè yígè de lái dào wáng gōng, shìzhe bǎ tuōxié chuān zài tāmen de jiǎo shàng. Dànshì tuōxié zǒngshì bǐ tāmen de jiǎo xiǎo yícùn. Wángguó zhōng méiyǒu yígè nǚrén kěyǐ chuān shàng nà zhǐ tuōxié.

Zhège shíhòu guówáng yǒudiǎn shēngqì le. "Zhège tuōxié shì cóng nǎlǐ lái de?" tā duì nóngfū dà jiào. Nóngfū shuō, tā bù zhīdào, tā zhǐshì kàndào tuōxié zài dìshàng, jiù bǎ tā ná le qǐlái. Guówáng bù xiāng

小，所以，每当有女人试着穿上拖鞋，拖鞋就会变得比女人的脚小一寸！因此，没有一个人能穿上它。

国王没有放弃。他叫陀汗的每个女人都试穿拖鞋。王国中的每个女人都一个一个地来到王宫，试着把拖鞋穿在她们的脚上。但是拖鞋总是比她们的脚小一寸。王国中没有一个女人可以穿上那只拖鞋。

这个时候国王有点生气了。"这个拖鞋是从哪里来的？"他对农夫大叫。农夫说，他不知道，他只是看到拖鞋在地上，就把它拿了起来。国王不相

xìn tā, yīncǐ tā bǎ nóngfū guān le qǐlai, bìng ràng tā de rén xiàng nóngfū wèn le xǔduō tiān. Dànshì nóngfū bù zhīdào xiézi shì cóng nǎlǐ lái de. Tā gàosù tāmen, tā shì zài Wú cūn de Dòng Jié shàng fāxiàn zhè zhī xiézi de. Guówáng zuìhòu fàng le nóngfū.

Nàtiān wǎnshàng, guówáng méiyǒu bànfǎ shuìzháo. Tā yìzhí zài xiǎngzhe nà zhī piàoliang de tuōxié, tā xūyào zhǎo chū shì shuí zuò de. Dì èr tiān, tā jíhé le tā de bīng hé jǐ sōu dà chuán, tāmen yuèguò hǎiyáng dào le Wú cūn. Guówáng gàosù tā de rén jiǎnchá cūnlǐ de měi dòng fángzi, bìngqiě ràng měi gè nǚrén shì chuān tuōxié. Rúguǒ yǒu nǚrén néng chuān shàng zhè zhī xié, jiù bǎ tā dài dào guówáng nàlǐ.

信他，因此他把农夫关了起来，并让他的人向农夫问了许多天。但是农夫不知道鞋子是从哪里来的。他告诉他们，他是在吴村的洞节上发现这只鞋子的。国王最后放了农夫。

那天晚上，国王没有办法睡着。他一直在想着那只漂亮的拖鞋，他需要找出是谁做的。第二天，他集合了他的兵和几艘大船，他们越过海洋到了吴村。国王告诉他的人检查村里的每栋房子，并且让每个女人试穿拖鞋。如果有女人能穿上这只鞋，就把她带到国王那里。

Tāmen yícì jìn yí dòng fángzi. Tāmen ràng
měi gè nǚrén shì chuān tuōxié, dànshì,
tuōxié dāngrán zǒngshì tài xiǎo. Zuìhòu
tāmen lái dào le Jīn hé tā de liǎng gè nǚ'ér
de jiālǐ. Shǒuxiān, tāmen ràng jìmǔ shì chuān
xiézi, dàn duì tā de jiǎo lái shuō, tuōxié tài
xiǎo le. Ránhòu, tāmen ràng jìmǔ de nǚ'ér
Jùnlì shì chuān xiézi, dàn tuōxié duì tā lái
shuō yě tài xiǎo le. "Zhè fángzi lǐ hái yǒu qítā
nǚrén ma?" qízhōng de yígè rén wèn. Jìmǔ
shuō, "Méiyǒu," dànshì tā de nǚ'ér huítóu
kàn le Yè Xiàn de fángjiān. Nà rén kàndào le
zhège, zài Yè Xiàn de fángjiān lǐ zhǎodào le
Yè Xiàn. Tāmen ràng tā chuān shàng tuōxié.
Tuōxié wánquán hé tā de jiǎo yíyàng dàxiǎo.
"Gēn wǒmen lái," tāmen gàosù tā.

他们一次进一栋房子。他们让每个女人试穿拖鞋，但是，拖鞋当然总是太小。最后他们来到了<u>金</u>和她的两个女儿的家里。首先，他们让继母试穿鞋子，但对她的脚来说，拖鞋太小了。然后，他们让继母的女儿<u>俊丽</u>试穿鞋子，但拖鞋对她来说也太小了。"这房子里还有其他女人吗？"其中的一个人问。继母说，"没有，"但是她的女儿回头看了<u>叶限</u>的房间。那人看到了这个，在<u>叶限</u>的房间里找到了<u>叶限</u>。他们让她穿上拖鞋。拖鞋完全和她的脚一样大小。"跟我们来，"他们告诉她。

"Qǐng děng yíxià, " Yè Xiàn shuō, "wǒ mǎshàng jiù lái." Tā guānshàng le fángjiān de mén. Tā tuō xià jiù yīfu, chuān shàng cānjiā Dòng Jié de yīfu: lánlǜsè de sīchóu cháng yī, cuì niǎo yǔmáo de dǒupéng hé jīnsè tuōxié. Ránhòu tā zǒuchū fángjiān, kàn qǐlái xiàng shì tiānshàng de nǚshén, shuō, "Wǒmen qù jiàn nǐmen de guówáng."

Dāng tā jiàndào guówáng de shíhòu, tā bǎ yíqiè dōu gàosù le tā. Tā gàosù tā tā de fùqīn shì Wú cūn de cūnzhǎng. Tā gàosù tā tā sǐqù de mǔqīn, tā de jìmǔ hé jìmèi, hé shuǐ táng lǐ yǒu mófǎ de yú. Tā hái gàosù tā tā de jìmǔ shā sǐ le yú, tiānshàng chūxiàn de nánrén, yǒu mófǎ de yú gǔ, Dòng Jié, hé tā shì zěnme diū le tā de tuōxié. Guówáng tīng le

"请等一下，"叶限说，"我马上就来。"她关上了房间的门。她脱下旧衣服，穿上参加洞节的衣服，蓝绿色的丝绸长衣，翠鸟羽毛的斗篷和金色拖鞋。然后她走出房间，看起来像是天上的女神，说，"我们去见你们的国王。"

当她见到国王的时候，她把一切都告诉了他。她告诉他她的父亲是吴村的村长。她告诉他她死去的母亲，她的继母和继妹，和水塘里有魔法的鱼。她还告诉他她的继母杀死了鱼，天上出现的男人，有魔法的鱼骨，洞节，和她是怎么丢了她的拖鞋。国王听了

zhè gè gùshì. Dāng tā tīngdào jìmǔ shā sǐ yú de shíhòu, tā fēicháng shēngqì.

"Shā sǐ yì zhī shénqí de dòngwù shì yí jiàn kěpà de shìqing," Guówáng shuō. "Yīncǐ, nǐ de jìmǔ hé jìmèi bìxū sǐ."

Dànshì Yè Xiàn shì gè hǎo nǚ'ér, duì jiārén shífēn zūnzhòng, tā shuō, "Wěidà de guówáng, qǐng búyào shā tāmen. Wǒ de jìmǔ zhǐshì xiǎng bāngzhù zìjǐ de nǚ'ér zhǎodào yígè hǎo zhàngfu, néng ràng tāmen liǎng gè guò shàng gèng hǎo de shēnghuó."

"Nǐ fēicháng shànliáng," Guówáng huídá. "Nǐ bǐ nǐ de jìmǔ gèng shànliáng. Dànshì wǒ huì ànzhào nǐ de yāoqiú qù zuò. Wǒ bú huì shā sǐ tāmen de."

这个故事。当他听到继母杀死鱼的时候，他非常生气。

"杀死一只神奇的动物是一件可怕的事情。"国王说，"因此，你的继母和继妹必须死。"

但是<u>叶限</u>是个好女儿，对家人十分尊重，她说，"伟大的国王，请不要杀他们。我的继母只是想帮助自己的女儿找到一个好丈夫，能让她们两个过上更好的生活。"

"你非常善良[43]，"国王回答。"你比你的继母更善良。但是我会按照你的要求去做。我不会杀死他们的。"

---

[43] 善良　　　shànliáng – kind, kindness

Ránhòu guówáng yào Yè Xiàn chéngwéi tā de qīzi, tā jiēshòu le. Tāmen liǎng gè dàizhe yú gǔtou huí dào le Tuóhàn wángguó. Tāmen jiéhūn le, Yè Xiàn chéngwéi le Tuóhàn de wánghòu.

Xiànzài nǐmen kěnéng rènwéi zhè gùshì yǐjīng jiéshù le. Dànshì wǒ bìxū gàosù nǐmen hòulái fāshēng de shìqing.

Guówáng réngrán duì jìmǔ shā sǐ yǒu mófǎ de yú ér shēngqì. Suǒyǐ tā méiyǒu ràng jìmǔ hé jìmèi gēn tāmen yìqǐ zhù zài wánggōng lǐ. Méiyǒu gěi jìmǔ liú xià qián, tā nǚ'ér néng hé yígè yǒu qián nánrén jiéhūn de xīwàng yě méiyǒu le. Yúshì, Jīn ràng tā de nǚ'ér dàitì Yè Xiàn zuò púrén. Zhè ràng Jùnlì fēicháng shēng

然后国王要叶限成为他的妻子，她接受了。他们两个带着鱼骨头回到了陀汪王国。他们结婚了，叶限成为了陀汪的王后[44]。

现在你们可能认为这故事已经结束了。但是我必须告诉你们后来发生的事情。

国王仍然对继母杀死有魔法的鱼而生气。所以他没有让继母和继妹跟他们一起住在王宫里。没有给继母留下钱，她女儿能和一个有钱男人结婚的希望也没有了。于是，金让她的女儿代替叶限做仆人。这让俊丽非常生

---

qì, tāmen liǎng gè zài tāmen shāndòng de fángzi lǐ zhēngchǎo le qǐlái. Tāmen hùxiāng dà jiào, yòng fángzi lǐ de dōngxi hùxiāng dǎ rén. Zài zhēngchǎo de shíhòu, tāmen de dòng dǎo le, tāmen liǎ dōu sǐ zài diào xià de shānshí xià.

Cūnlǐ de rénmen bǎ liǎng gè sǐqù de nǚrén cóng shāndòng lǐ lā chūlái, bǎ tāmen mái zài yígè jiàozuò "Èr Nǚ Mù" de dìfāng. Hòulái, cūnlǐ de rén xiāngxìn liǎng gè sǐqù de nǚrén chéng le nǚshén. Cūnlǐ rén xiāngxìn nǚshén kěyǐ bāngzhù yǒu àiqíng wèntí de rén. Méiyǒu jiéhūn de nánrén hé nǚrén lái dào mù qián, xiàng nǚshén qǐngqiú bāngzhù tāmen zhǎo qīzi huòzhě zhàngfu. Yǒu de shíhòu, niánqīng de nánrén hé nǚrén lái qǐngqiú nǚ

气，他们两个在他们山洞的房子里争吵[45]了起来。他们互相大叫，用房子里的东西互相打人。在争吵的时候，他们的洞倒[46]了，他们俩都死在掉下的山石下。

村里的人们把两个死去的女人从山洞里拉出来，把她们埋[47]在一个叫做"二女墓"的地方。后来，村里的人相信两个死去的女人成了女神。村里人相信女神可以帮助有爱情问题的人。没有结婚的男人和女人来到墓前，向女神请求帮助他们找妻子或者丈夫。有的时候，年轻的男人和女人来请求女

---

[45] 争吵　zhēngchǎo – to quarrel
[46] 倒　dǎo – to fall
[47] 埋　mái – to bury

shén bāngzhù, ràng tāmen zhǎodào nǚ
péngyǒu huò nán péngyǒu. Yǒu de shíhòu,
qīzi lái zhèlǐ, qídǎo yǒu yígè nánhái huòzhě
nǚhái.

Yè Xiàn hé guówáng zhù zài Tuóhàn, tāmen
xìngfú de zài yìqǐ shēnghuó le dàyuē yì nián.
Dàn guówáng ài qián hé měilì de dōngxi
duōguò ài tā de qīzi. Guówáng jīngcháng huì
xiàng shàngtiān qídǎo néng dédào jīnzi, néng
ràng yú gǔ gěi tā dài lái jīnzi. Dànshì dào le dì
èr nián, yú gǔtou biàn lèi le, huòzhě tāmen
zhǐshì bùxiǎng zài bāngzhù guówáng le, suǒyǐ
tāmen bú zài gěi tā jīnzi. Yīncǐ, guówáng bǎ
yú gǔtou hé yìxiē jīnzi, dōu mái zài hǎibiān.

神帮助，让他们找到女朋友或男朋友。有的时候，妻子来这里，祈祷有一个男孩或者女孩。

叶限和国王住在<u>陀汗</u>，他们幸福地在一起生活了大约一年。但国王爱钱和美丽的东西多过爱他的妻子。国王经常会向上天祈祷能得到金子，能让鱼骨给他带来金子。但是到了第二年，鱼骨头变累了，或者它们只是不想再帮助国王了，所以它们不再给他金子。因此，国王把鱼骨头和一些金子，都埋在海边。

Jǐ nián yǐhòu, guówáng xūyào jīnzi, suǒyǐ tā qù hǎibiān wā jīnzi hé yú gǔ. Dāng tā zài wā jīnzi de shíhòu, fāshēng le yì chǎng dà fēngbào. Hǎishuǐ shàngshēng, suǒyǒu de yú gǔtou dōu bèi hǎishuǐ dài zǒu le. Yú gǔtou xiàng yǔmáo yíyàng qīng. Suǒyǐ zài shuǐmiàn shàng, dōu bèi hǎi niǎo dài zǒu le.

Jǐ nián yǐhòu, guówáng sǐ le, Yè Xiàn chéngwéi Tuóhàn de tǒngzhì zhě. Tā shì yígè cōngming hé shànliáng de nǔwáng, Tuóhàn de rénmen dōu ài tā. Tā tǒngzhì le hěnduō nián.

Dāng tā biàn dé hěn lǎo de shíhòu, Yè Xiàn zuò chuán huí dào Wú cūn. Tā zǒu jìn shānlǐ, yìzhí lái dào tā yǐqián zhùguò de shāndòng.

几年以后，国王需要金子，所以他去海边挖[48]金子和鱼骨。当他在挖金子的时候，发生了一场大风暴。海水上升[49]，所有的鱼骨头都被海水带走了。鱼骨头像羽毛一样轻。所以在水面上，都被海鸟带走了。

几年以后，国王死了，叶限成为陀汗的统治者[50]。她是一个聪明和善良的女王，陀汗的人们都爱她。她统治了很多年。

当她变得很老的时候，叶限坐船回到吴村。她走进山里，一直来到她以前住过的山洞。

---

[48] 挖　　　　wā – to dig
[49] 升　　　　shēng – to rise up
[50] 统治者　　tǒngzhì zhě – ruler

Shāndòng de qiánmiàn yǒu yì kē měilì de lǎo shù, cóng tā mǔqīn de fénmù lǐ zhǎng chūlái. Zài shù de zhōuwéi, dōu shì hǎi niǎo dài lái de yú gǔ. Yè Xiàn bǎ zìjǐ bāo zài dǒupéng lǐ, tǎng zài zhōuwéi dōu shì yú gǔ de dìshàng, bǎtóu fàng zài shù gēn shàng, shuìzháo le.

山洞的前面有一棵美丽的老树，从她母亲的坟墓里长出来。在树的周围，都是海鸟带来的鱼骨。叶限把自己包在斗篷里，躺在周围都是鱼骨的地上，把头放在树根[51]上，睡着了。

---

[51] 根   gēn – tree root

Ye Xian

My dear children, let me tell you a story that I heard from my mother. She heard the story from her mother, and she heard it from a man named Li. Long ago, Li worked in my grandparents' house. He was from the south of China. He knew many stories of gods and monsters that were passed down from the Zhuang people who lived in that region. This is a story he told to my grandmother. I think you will like it!

This story is from a long time ago, before the Qin and before the Han. At that time there were people living in the area that we now call Guangxi. These people called themselves the Zhuang. There was a village in this area called Wu. The people in the village of Wu mostly lived in mountain caves near the ocean. They ate fish and grew rice in the mountains. The leader of the village was a man named Wu Dong.

Wu Dong had two wives. This was common among Zhuang leaders of that time. We don't know the name of his first wife, but we know that she had one daughter, a girl named Ye Xian. Ye Xian was beautiful and very bright. She also had many skills. She could do women's work such as making clothes, cooking and cleaning. And she also knew how to turn gold into beautiful golden thread.

Wu Dong's second wife was named Jin. Jin had her own daughter named Junli, who was younger than Ye Xian.

Junli did not like to work, and she did not show respect to her older sister Ye Xian.

Wu Dong was a good leader and a good man. He loved both of his wives and both of his daughters. But his first wife died, and a few years later, Wu Dong also became sick and died.

Among the Zhuang people, when the village leader dies, his oldest son becomes the new leader. But Wu Dong had no sons. So the people of Wu had to choose a new village leader from a different family.

Ye Xian, Jin and Junli had all been part of the village leader's family. But when Wu Dong died and the new village leader was named, they were not part of his family. They had nothing. They had to leave the village leader's big house. They went to live in a small cave in the mountains like the other villagers. They had to catch their own fish and grow their own rice.

Jin loved her own daughter, but she did not love Ye Xian. She made Ye Xian a servant in her house. She made Ye Xian do all the cooking and cleaning, but she also gave Ye Xian other more dangerous work. Sometimes Ye Xian had to get firewood from dangerous places in the mountains. Sometimes she had to fetch water from deep wells. But Ye Xian did not say anything. She worked hard every day. She had no friends and she had no time to play or study.

One day, Jin told Ye Xian to get water from a deep well. Ye Xian went to the well and pulled up a bucket of water. She saw something in the bucket. She looked more closely and saw it was a small fish. The fish was two inches long, with red fins and golden eyes. She thought the fish was beautiful. She did not know that the fish was really her dead mother, who had returned to help her daughter.

Ye Xian did not have any friends, so she decided that the little fish would become her friend. So she put the fish in a bowl. She did not tell her stepmother or her stepsister about the fish.

Every day she gave a little bit of her own food to the fish, and every day the fish ate the food and became a little bit bigger. Soon the fish was too big for the bowl, so Ye Xian moved the fish to a bigger bowl, and then an even bigger bowl, and then a large bucket. Still the fish kept growing. Soon there was nothing large enough to hold the fish. So Ye Xian put the fish in a pond. The fish grew and grew until it was almost ten feet long.

Every day Ye Xian gave food to the fish. She pushed the food down under the water so the fish could eat it. Whenever Ye Xian came to the pond, the fish stuck its head out of the water and rested its head on the shore. Ye Xian rested her head on the fish's head, looked up at the sky, and talked to the fish. The girl told the fish about her problems and her dreams. The fish listened but never said anything.

Ye Xian loved the fish, and the fish loved Ye Xian. But the fish was careful. If anyone else came close to the pond, the fish swam down to hide at the bottom of the pond.

One day the stepmother looked out from the house and saw Ye Xian and the fish together. She did not understand what the girl and the fish were doing, but she liked to eat fish. So the stepmother waited until Ye Xian returned to the house, then the stepmother walked out to the pond to look at the fish. But the fish was hiding at the bottom of the pond, and even though Jin looked very closely, she could not see it.

The stepmother really wanted to catch the fish and eat it. So she said to Ye Xian, "My dear daughter, you have been working too hard. I want to give you a new jacket. Take off your old clothes and put on this nice new jacket." Ye Xian was happy to have new clothes, so she took off her old clothes and put on the jacket. "You look very nice," said the stepmother sweetly, "now go to the well at the bottom of the mountain and collect some water." This well was several miles away, but Ye Xian did as she was told.

As soon as the girl was out of sight, the stepmother took off her own clothes and put on the girl's clothes. Then she picked up a knife and hid it in her sleeve. She went to the pond and called to the fish. The fish saw the stepmother but thought it was Ye Xian, so it stuck out its head out of the water. Quickly the stepmother killed the fish with the knife. Then she brought the fish into the house, made a fish dinner, and ate it. It was a very tasty meal, twice as tasty as the flesh of other fish.

The stepmother did not want Ye Xian to know what she did. So she threw the fish's bones into the dung pile behind the house. And she did not give any of the food to Ye Xian. Instead, she just gave Ye Xian some rice.

The next day Ye Xian went back to the pond to see her friend the fish. She called again and again to the fish, but it did not come. After a long time she knew that the fish was gone. She sat down at the edge of the pond and cried.

Suddenly, she heard a sound. She looked up and saw a man flying in the sky. The man flew down and stood in front of her. He was very tall, he wore a long white robe, and he had long white hair that flew in all directions.

The man said to Ye Xian, "Don't cry. Your stepmother killed the fish and ate it for dinner last night. She threw its bones into the dung pile. Go there and find the bones. Hide them in your room. Put the bones in four pots, and put those pots under the four corners of your bed. I must tell you that the fish was a magic fish, and its bones are magic bones. If you need anything, just pray to the gods, and the bones will help you get your wish."

The girl did as the man told her. She went to the dung pile and found the fish's bones. She picked up all the bones and carried them into her room and hid them under the bed in four pots.

She was very hungry, but of course she did not want to eat the fish that her stepmother had prepared. So she prayed to the gods for food. Right away a delicious pot of vegetable dumplings appeared in front of her. She ate all the dumplings. Then she prayed to the gods for some nice new clothing and that appeared too. She put on the clothes. Then she held a small mirror in her hand and looked at herself. She said to herself, "I think that with these nice clothes, I could go to the Cave Festival!"

The annual Cave Festival was the following week. All the young people from all the nearby villages came to the festival to sing and dance and meet other young people, and find someone to marry. Ye Xian really wanted to go to the Cave Festival, but her stepmother told her to stay home. This was because Jin wanted her own daughter to find a good husband, and she did not want the bright and beautiful Ye Xian nearby. "You stay here," Jin said to Ye Xian. "Keep an eye on the fruit tree in the courtyard and make sure nobody takes any of our fruit."

Ye Xian was a good daughter. She always tried to show great respect to her stepmother and do everything that the stepmother told her. But she also really wanted to go to the Cave Festival. "What should I do?" she asked herself. She decided to pray to the gods for beautiful clothing to wear to the festival. If the gods gave her the clothing, then she would go. If not, then she would stay home and watch the fruit tree in the courtyard.

Ye Xian waited until her stepmother and stepsister were out of sight. Then she sat down in front of the fish bones and she prayed to the gods for beautiful clothing to wear to the festival. Right away she received a beautiful long gown made of blue-green silk, a cloak made of kingfisher feathers, and a pair of slippers made from silk and gold thread. She cried with happiness. She put on the new clothes and went to the Cave Festival. The people at the festival saw her and thought she was a beautiful princess, and many of the men wanted to marry her.

Of course, Jin and her daughter Junli were also at the Cave Festival, where Jin was trying to find a good husband for Junli. Jin was talking with some young men about her daughter. Suddenly Junli looked up and saw Ye Xian. She said to her mother, "See that girl over there with the cloak made of kingfisher feathers? Doesn't she look a lot like my elder sister?" The stepmother looked and saw her too.

Ye Xian knew that they were looking at her. So she turned and ran away as fast as she could. She ran so fast that one of the golden slippers came off her foot. She ran all the way back to her home, wearing just one slipper. When she got home, she was so tired that she didn't even go into the cave. She just wrapped an old cloak around her body and walked to her mother's grave, which was in the courtyard. Then she lay down on the ground, put her arms around the fruit tree that was growing on her mother's grave, and fell asleep.

Later that evening, the stepmother and the stepdaughter returned home. They both saw Ye Xian sleeping with her arms around the fruit tree in the courtyard. They decided that she could not have been at the Cave Festival, so they thought no more about it.

When Ye Xian was at the Cave Festival, a farmer from the village was also at the festival, talking with some friends not far from where Ye Xian had been standing. The farmer saw Ye Xian run away, and he also saw the golden slipper come off her foot. So he walked over and picked up the slipper. He looked at the slipper and saw that it was made of silk and golden thread, so he knew it was valuable. He decided to try and sell the slipper.

But where should he sell it, and who should he sell it to? He thought about this problem for a long time. He needed to find a rich man who would not ask questions about where the slipper came from. Then he suddenly knew what he should do. He would go to Tuohan, which was a large nation across the ocean. He had heard that the king of Tuohan was a young man, very powerful, very wealthy, and he had many soldiers. The farmer had also heard that the king of Tuohan loved beautiful things more than he loved people.

So the farmer gave money to a boatman to take him across the ocean to Tuohan. This took three days. When he arrived in Tuohan he gave money to some people to introduce him to the king.

"Who are you, and why are you here?" asked the king.

"Great king, I have something I think you would be interested in," the farmer replied. Then he showed the slipper to the king.

The king saw the slipper and immediately fell in love with it. The slipper was as bright as the sun, as light as a feather, and it did not make any noise, not even on stones. The king bought it from the farmer. Then the king thought, "This slipper is so beautiful, I wonder how beautiful is the woman who made it and wore it!" So he decided to find the woman who made the slipper.

He ordered every woman in his palace to try on the slipper. But the slipper had magic. It would change its size, so whenever a woman tried to put the slipper on, the slipper would become an inch smaller than the woman's foot! So none of them could put it on.

The king did not give up. He ordered that every woman in Tuohan should try on the slipper. One by one, every woman in the kingdom came to the king's palace and tried to put the slipper on their foot. But the slipper was always an inch smaller than her foot. No woman in the kingdom could wear it.

Now the king was getting a little bit angry. "Where did this slipper come from?" he shouted at the farmer. The farmer said that he did not know, he just saw the slipper on the ground and picked it up. The king did not believe him, so he threw the farmer in jail and had his men question him for many days. But the farmer simply did not know where the shoe came from. He told the men that found the shoe at the Cave Festival in the village of Wu. Finally the king let the farmer go.

That night, the king could not sleep. He kept thinking about the beautiful slipper, and he needed to find out who made it. So the next day he gathered his soldiers and several large ships, and they sailed across the ocean to the Wu village. The king told his men to search every house in the village, and make every woman try on the slipper. If any woman could wear that shoe, the men were to bring her to the king.

The men entered every house, one at a time. They told every woman to try on the slipper, but of course the slipper was always too small. Finally they came to the house of Jin and her two daughters. First they told the stepmother to try on the shoe, but the slipper was too small for her foot. Then they told the stepmother's daughter Junli to try on the shoe, but the slipper was too small for her too. "Are there any other women in this house?" asked one of the men. The stepmother said "No," but her daughter looked back towards Ye Xian's room. The men saw this and found Ye Xian in her room. They told her to put on the slipper. It fit her foot perfectly. "Come with us," they told her.

"Please wait a minute," said Ye Xian, "I will be right with you." She closed the door to her room. She took off her old clothes and put on the clothes that she had worn to the Cave Festival: the blue-green silk gown, the cloak of kingfisher feathers, and the golden slippers. Then she came out of her room, looking like a goddess from heaven, and said, "Let's go and meet your king."

When she met the king, she told him everything. She told him about her father, the leader of Wu. She told him about her dead mother, her stepmother and stepsister, and the magical fish in the pond. She told him about her stepmother killing the fish, the visit from the man from the sky, the magic fish bones, the Cave Festival, and how she lost her slipper. The king listened to the story. He was very angry when he heard about the stepmother killing the fish.

"It is a terrible thing to kill a magical animal," said the king. "Because of this, your stepmother and stepsister must die."

But Ye Xian was a good daughter, and showing respect to her family, she said, "great king, please do not kill them. My stepmother was only trying to help her own daughter find a good husband, so that the two of them could have a better life."

"You are very kind," replied the king. "You are more kind than your stepmother. But I will do as you ask. I will not have them killed."

Then the king asked Ye Xian to be his wife, and she accepted. The two of them returned to the kingdom of Tuohan, taking the fish bones with them. They were married, and Ye Xian became the queen of Tuohan.

Now you might think this is the end of the story. But I must tell you what happened later.

The king was still angry about the stepmother killing the magic fish. So he did not let the stepmother and stepsister come and live in the royal palace. The stepmother was left with no money, and no hope that her daughter would be able to marry a wealthy man. So Jin made her daughter a servant, to take the place of Ye Xian. This made Junli very angry, and the two of them had a big fight in their cave house. They shouted at each other, and they hit each other with things that were in the house. During the fight their cave fell down and both of them died under falling rocks.

The people of the village pulled the two dead women from the cave, and buried them in a place called the Tomb of the Two Women. Afterwards, the people of the village believed that two dead women became goddesses.

The village people believed that the goddesses could help people who had problems with love. Unmarried men and women visited the tomb to ask the goddesses for help in finding a wife or husband. Sometimes younger men and women came to ask the goddesses for help in finding a girlfriend or boyfriend. And wives sometimes came and prayed to have a baby boy or a baby girl.

Ye Xian and the king lived in Tuohan, and they lived happily together for about a year. But the king loved money and beautiful things more than he loved his wife. Often the king would pray to the gods for gold, and the fish bones would give gold to him. But by the second year, the bones became tired, or maybe they just didn't want to help the king anymore, so they stopped giving him gold. So the king buried the fish bones on the seashore, along with some gold, along with some gold.

A few years later the king needed the gold, so he went to the seashore and dug up the gold and the fish bones. While he was digging up the gold, there was a big storm. The ocean rose up, and all of the fish bones were taken away by the sea. The fish bones were as light as a feather. They stayed on the surface of the water and were all picked up by sea birds and carried away.

Several years after that, the king died and Ye Xian became the ruler of Tuohan. She was a wise and kind queen, and the people of Tuohan loved her. She ruled for many years.

When she became very old, Ye Xian traveled by boat back to the village of Wu. She walked up into the mountains, until she arrived at the cave where she used to live. In front of the cave was a beautiful old tree that was growing from the grave of her mother. On the ground around the tree were all the fish bones that had been carried by the sea birds. Ye Xian wrapped a cloak around herself, lay down on the ground surrounded by the fish bones, rested her head on a tree root, and went to sleep.

Proper Nouns

These are all the Chinese proper nouns used in this book.

Chinese	Pinyin	English
洞节	Dòng Jié	Cave Festival
二女墓	Èr Nǚ Mù	Tomb of the Two Women
广西	Guǎngxī	Guanxi, a province in China
汉	Hàn	Han Dynasty
金	Jīn	Jin, stepmother of Ye Xian
俊丽	Jùnlì	Junli, daughter of Jin
李	Lǐ	Li, a man's name
秦	Qín	Qin Dynasty
陀汗	Tuóhàn	Tuohan, a kingdom
吴	Wú	Wu, a village
吴东	Wú Dōng	Wu Dong, father of Ye Xian
叶限	Yè Xiàn	Ye Xian
中国	Zhōngguó	China
壮	Zhuàng	Zhuang, a tribe

Glossary

These are all the Chinese words (other than proper nouns) used in this book.

Chinese	Pinyin	English
啊	a	ah, oh, what
爱	ài	to love
爱情	àiqíng	love
按照	ànzhào	according to
把	bǎ	to hold, to grasp
白	bái	white, bright
白发	báifà	white hair
搬	bān	to move
办法	bànfǎ	way, method
帮助	bāngzhù	to help
抱	bào	to hold, to carry
包	bāo	to wrap, package
保证	bǎozhèng	to ensure
倍	bèi	times (multiply)
臂	bì	arm
比	bǐ	to compare
变(成)	biàn(chéng)	change
表示	biǎoshì	to express
别	bié	do not
兵	bīng	soldier
并且	bìngqiě	furthermore
必须	bìxū	to have to
不	bù	no, not
部分	bùfen	part
菜	cài	food, vegetable
藏	cáng	to hide
参加	cānjiā	to participate in

差不多	chàbuduō	almost, nearly
唱歌	chànggē	to sing
成（为）	chéng(wéi)	to become
尺	chǐ	Chinese foot
吃	chī	to eat
出	chū	to go/come out
船	chuán	ship
穿	chuān	to wear
船夫	chuánfū	boatman
床	chuáng	bed
出现	chūxiàn	to appear
次	cì	next in a sequence
从	cóng	from
聪明	cōngming	clever, bright
翠鸟	cuì niǎo	kingfisher
寸	cùn	Chinese inch
村（庄）	cun(zhuang)	village
村长	cūnzhǎng	village head
大	dà	big, great
打	dǎ	to hit
带	dài	belt
代替	dàitì	to replace
但（是）	dàn(shì)	however, but
当	dāng	when, be
当然	dāngrán	of course
当时	dāngshí	at that time
到	dào	to arrive, towards
刀	dāo	knife
倒	dǎo	to fall
打扫	dǎsǎo	to clean
大小	dàxiǎo	size
地	de	land, (adverbial particle)

的	de	of
得	dé	(particle showing degree or possibility)
等	děng	to wait
底	dǐ	bottom
点	diǎn	spot
掉	diào	to fall, to drop
地方	dìfang	location, place
丢	diū	to lose
栋	dòng	(measure word for buildings, houses)
洞	dòng	cave
动物	dòngwù	animal
东西	dōngxi	thing
都	dōu	all
斗篷	dǒupéng	cloak
对	duì	to, for
堆	duī	a heap or pile
顿	dùn	(measure word for non-repeating actions)
多	duō	many
饿	è	hunger
而	ér	and
儿子	érzi	son
发出	fāchū	to send
放	fàng	to release
房（子）	fang (zi)	house
房间	fángjiān	room
放弃	fàngqì	to give up
发生	fāshēng	to happen
发现	fāxiàn	to find
飞	fei	to fly
非常	fēicháng	extreme, unusual
粪	fèn	manure

分	fēn	to divide, a minute
坟 (墓)	fén(mù)	grave
风暴	fēngbào	storm
富	fù	rich
附近	fùjìn	nearby
父亲	fùqīn	father
改变	gǎibiàn	to change
高	gāo	high
告诉	gàosu	to tell
高兴	gāoxìng	happy
个	gè	(measure word, generic)
各	gè	each, every
给	gěi	to give
跟	gēn	follow
根	gēn	tree root
更	gèng	watch (2-hour period)
宫 (殿)	gōng(diàn)	palace
公主	gōngzhǔ	princess
工作	gōngzuò	work
骨 (头)	gǔ(tóu)	bone
关	guān	to shut down
罐 (子)	guàn(zi)	pot
关于	guānyú	about
贵重	guìzhòng	precious
过	guò	to pass
锅	guō	pot
国 (家)	guó(jiā)	country
国王	guówáng	king
故事	gùshi	story
还	hái	still
海 (洋)	hǎi(yáng)	ocean
孩子	háizi	child

好	hǎo	good
和	hé	and
很	hěn	very
红(色)	hóng(sè)	red
后来	hòulái	later
后面	hòumiàn	behind
回	huí	return
会	huì	can, will
回答	huídá	to reply
或者	huòzhě	perhaps
互相	hùxiāng	each other
几	jǐ	several
家	jiā	home, family
件	jiàn	piece
见(面)	jiàn (miàn)	to see, to meet
检查	jiǎnchá	to inspect
叫	jiào	to call, to yell
角	jiǎo	angle, horn
脚	jiǎo	foot
饺子	jiǎozi	dumplings
结婚	jiéhūn	to marry
姐姐	jiějie	older sister
节日	jiérì	festival
介绍	jièshào	to introduce
接受	jiēshòu	to accept
结束	jiéshù	to finish
集合	jíhé	aggregate
继妹	jìmèi	stepsister
继母	jìmǔ	stepmother
近	jìn	near
进	jìn	to enter
金(子)	jīn(zi)	golden

技能	jìnéng	skill
井	jǐng	well
经常	jīngcháng	often
镜子	jìngzi	mirror
继女	jìnǚ	stepdaughter
即使	jíshǐ	even if
就	jiù	just, right away
旧	jiù	old, worn
久	jiǔ	long (time)
觉得	juéde	to think
决定	juédìng	to decide
看（见）	kàn(jiàn)	to see
可能	kěnéng	probable
可怕	kěpà	terrible
可以	kěyǐ	can, may
哭	kū	to cry
快	kuài	fast
拉	lā	to pull
来	lái	to come, to arrive
蓝	lán	blue
老	lǎo	old
了	le	(indicates completion)
累	lèi	tired
里（面）	li (miàn)	inside
俩	liǎ	both
亮	liàng	bright
两	liǎng	two
聊天	liáotiān	chat
离开	líkāi	to leave
另	lìng	another
例如	lìrú	for example
留	liú	to leave, to stay

绿（色）	lǜ (sè)	green
吗	ma	(indicates a question)
卖	mài	to sell
买	mǎi	to buy
埋	mái	to bury
马上	mǎshàng	right away
每	měi	each
美（丽）	měi(lì)	beautiful
没（有）	méi(yǒu)	no, have not
门	mén	door
梦	mèng	dream
米（饭）	mǐ(fàn)	rice
名（字）	míng(zi)	name
明白	míngbai	to understand
魔（法）	mó(fǎ)	magic
魔力	mólì	magic
木柴	mùchái	firewood
母亲	mǔqīn	mother
拿	ná	to hold, to take
那儿	nà'er	there
奶奶	nǎinai	grandma
那里	nàlǐ	there
南（方）	nán(fāng)	south
男孩	nánhái	boy
那是	nàshì	that is
呢	ne	(indicates question)
能	néng	to be able to
你	nǐ	you
年	nián	year
年轻	niánqīng	young
鸟	niǎo	bird
农夫	nóngfū	farmer

女儿	nǚ'ér	daughter
女孩	nǚhái	girl
努力	nǔlì	to strive
女人	nǚrén	woman
跑	pǎo	to run
朋友	péngyou	friend
漂亮	piàoliang	beautiful
仆（人）	pū(rén)	servant
普遍	pǔbiàn	common
鳍	qí	fin
钱	qián	money
前（面）	qián(miàn)	front
强大	qiángdà	powerful
祈祷	qídao	to pray
起来	qǐlái	(after verb, indicates start of an action)
亲爱	qīn'ài	dear
请	qǐng	to ask, please
轻	qīng	light
请求	qǐngqiú	to request
其实	qíshí	actually
其他	qítā	other
其中	qízhōng	among
妻子	qīzi	wife
去	qù	to go
取	qǔ	to take off
让	ràng	to let, to cause
然后	ránhòu	then
人	rén	person, people
扔	rēng	to throw
仍然	réngrán	still
任何	rènhé	whatever, any
人们	rénmen	people

人世	rénshì	the world
认为	rènwéi	to think
如果	rúguǒ	if
三	sān	three
色	sè	color
杀	shā	to kill
山	shān	mountain
上	shàng	top, on, first
上天	shàngtian	god
善良	shànliáng	kind, kindness
谁	shéi	who
神	shén	god, immortal
身	shēn	body
深	shēn	deep
伸	shēn	to stretch out
升	shēng	to rise up
生病	shēngbìng	to fall ill
生活	shēnghuó	life
生气	shēngqì	anger
声音	shēngyīn	voice
什么	shénme	what?
神奇	shénqí	magical
甚至	shènzhì	so much so
十	shí	ten
是	shì	is, yes
试	shì	to taste, to try
石（头）	shí (tou)	stone
时（候）	shí(hou)	time
事（情）	shì(qing)	thing, affair
时间	shíjiān	time
手	shǒu	hand
收拾	shōushi	tidy

首先	shǒuxiān	first
树	shù	tree
双	shuāng	double
水	shuǐ	water
睡（觉）	shuì(jiào)	to sleep
水果	shuǐguǒ	fruit
水面	shuǐmiàn	water surface
睡着	shuìzhào	asleep
说（话）	shuō(huà)	to speak
四	sì	four
死	sǐ	to die
丝绸	sīchóu	silk
丝线	sīxiàn	silk thread
艘	sōu	(measure word for ships)
所以	suǒyǐ	therefore, so
所有	suǒyǒu	all
他	tā	he, him
它	tā	it
她	tā	she, her
抬	tái	to lift
太	tài	too much
塘	táng	pond
躺	tǎng	to lie down
甜	tián	sweet
天	tiān	sky, day
条	tiáo	(measure word for narrow, flexible things)
跳舞	tiàowǔ	to dance
听	tīng	to listen, to hear
桶	tǒng	bucket
统治	tǒngzhì	to rule
统治者	tǒngzhì zhě	ruler

头	tóu	head
推	tuī	to push
脱	tuō	to take off
拖鞋	tuōxié	slipper
突然	tūrán	suddenly
挖	wā	to dig
外	wài	abroad, outside
完	wán	to finish
玩	wán	to play
碗	wǎn	bowl
往	wǎng	to, towards
王后	wánghòu	queen
完全	wánquán	completely
为	wèi	for
伟大	wěidà	great
危险	wēixiǎn	danger
问	wèn	to ask
问题	wèntí	problem, question
我	wǒ	I, me
屋子	wūzi	house
下（面）	xià	lower, below
线	xiàn	thread, line
像	xiàng	looks like
向	xiàng	towards
想	xiǎng	to think
相信	xiāngxìn	to believe
现在	xiànzài	now
小	xiǎo	small
小心	xiǎoxīn	to be careful
些	xiē	some
喜欢	xǐhuan	to like
新	xīn	new

幸福	xìngfú	happiness
星期	xīngqī	week
兴趣	xìngqù	interest in
辛苦	xīnkǔ	hard
袖(子)	xiù(zi)	sleeve
希望	xīwàng	to hope
需(要)	xū(yào)	to need
许多	xǔduō	many
学习	xuéxí	to study
眼(睛)	yǎn(jing)	eye
要	yào	to want
也	yě	also
爷爷	yéye	grandpa
一	yī	one
衣(服)	yī(fu)	clothes
一边	yìbiān	one side
以后	yǐhòu	after, later, in future
已经	yǐjīng	already
一面	yímiàn	one side
因此	yīncǐ	therefore
应该	yīnggāi	should
因为	yīnwèi	because
以前	yǐqián	before
一切	yíqiè	everything
以为	yǐwéi	to believe
一样	yíyàng	equally
一直	yìzhí	always
用	yòng	to use
又	yòu	also
有	yǒu	to have
游(泳)	yóu (yǒng)	to swim, to tour
鱼	yú	fish

与	yǔ	and, with
远	yuǎn	far
院子	yuànzi	courtyard
越	yuè	to exceed
羽毛	yǔmáo	feather
于是	yúshì	therefore
再	zài	again
在	zài	located at
怎么	zěnme	how?
站	zhàn	stand
长	zhǎng	grow
丈夫	zhàngfu	husband
长老	zhǎnglǎo	elder
找	zhǎo	to look for
着	zhe	with
这	zhè	this, these
真	zhēn	true, real
争吵	zhēngchǎo	to quarrel
只	zhī	(measure word for animals)
之	zhī	of
知道	zhīdào	to know
之前	zhīqián	before
种	zhòng	to grow
中	zhōng	among
中国	zhōngguó	China
周围	zhōuwéi	surroundings
住	zhù	to live
抓	zhuā	catch
转(身)	zhuǎn(shēn)	to turn around
准备	zhǔnbèi	preparation
自己	zìjǐ	own, self
仔细	zǐxì	careful

总是	zǒngshì	always
走	zǒu	to walk, to go
最后	zuìhòu	last
尊重	zūnzhòng	to respect
做	zuò	to do, to make
坐	zuò	to sit, to ride
昨晚	zuó wǎn	last night

Further Reading

The Ye Xian story first appeared in the following book, which is not available online but can be purchased on Amazon.

- Duan Chengshi, *Miscellaneous Morsels from Youyang (Youyang Zazu 酉阳杂组),* Beijing: Zhonghua, 1981.

If you're interested in taking a deep dive into the history, cultural background and symbolism of the Ye Xian story, Mila Moioli's Ph.D. thesis is the best place to look. It's an extremely detailed analysis (nearly 300 pages) of the story. At the end, Moioli reprints the complete original story from Duan Chengshi's book, in Simplified Chinese and English.

- Moioli, Mila. *Ye Xian and Her Sisters: The Role of a Tang Story in the Cinderella Cycle*. Ph.D. thesis, Free University of Barcelona, Department of Traditions, Interpretation and Studies of Asian Culture. 2018. Retrieved from www.tdx.cat/bitstream/handle/10803/462102/mimo1de1.pdf?sequence=1 .

Other good articles and papers that are available online include:

- Beauchamp, Fay. *Asian Origins of Cinderella: The Zhuang Storyteller of Guangxi*. 2010. Retrieved from mospace.umsystem.edu/xmlui/bitstream/handle/10355/65210/OralTradition25-2-Beauchamp.pdf?sequence=1&isAllowed=y .

- Heiner, Heidi Ann. Introduction to *Cinderella Tales From Around the World*. SurLaLune Press. Retrieved from forlackofsomegoodwriting.files.wordpress.com/2013/05/searchingforcinderella.pdf .

- Zhang, Aidong. *Cinderella in Different Dresses: From A Narrative Perspective*. International Journal of Languages, Literature and Linguistics, Vol. 4, No. 3, September 2018. Retrieved from www.ijlll.org/vol4/170-IC0072.pdf .

- Basile, Giambattista. *The Cat Cinderella*. Reprinted from *The Pentamerone of Giambattista Basile*, ed. N. M. Penzer, John Lane (London), 1932. Retrieved from bookcandy.typepad.com/files/cinderella-variants.pdf .

QR codes for each of these web addresses are on the next page. If you take a picture of the QR code with your smartphone camera, you'll be able to go directly to that web page. These QR codes do <u>not</u> use any tracking software.

Moioli, Mila. *Ye Xian and Her Sisters: The Role of a Tang Story in the Cinderella Cycle.*

Beauchamp, Fay. *Asian Origins of Cinderella: The Zhuang Storyteller of Guangxi.*

Heiner, Heidi Ann. *Introduction to Cinderella Tales From Around the World.*

Zhang, Aidong. *Cinderella in Different Dresses: From A Narrative Perspective.*

Basile, Giambattista. *The Cat Cinderella.*

About the Authors

Jeff Pepper (author) is President and CEO of Imagin8 Press, and has written dozens of books about Chinese language and culture. Over his thirty-five year career he has founded and led several successful computer software firms, including one that became a publicly traded company. He's authored two software related books and was awarded three U.S. patents.

Dr. Xiao Hui Wang (translator) has an M.S. in Information Science, an M.D. in Medicine, a Ph.D. in Neurobiology and Neuroscience, and 25 years experience in academic and clinical research. She has taught Chinese for over 10 years and has extensive experience in translating Chinese to English and English to Chinese.

Printed in Great Britain
by Amazon

38799833R00059